ODE TO JOY

ODE TO JOY

A Winklebrig's Tale

Charles Harker

Jardine Press 2010
ISBN 978-0-9552035-9-6
Text © Charles Harker
Drawings © Janet Harker

CONTENTS

page 1   Early Days

page 8   Mersea Hack Boat

page 12   Winklebrig

page 17   The Fleet

page 23   Scotland

page 25   Swallowed by The Quicksand

page 29   "...... Like Aphrodite"

page 31   Home Again

page 33   Old Friends

page 36   Cornwall and the River Fal

page 38   The Creek Where Time Stands Still

page 41   The Secret River

page 44   The World Beyond

page 47   The Festival

page 52   Retired to the Norfolk Broads

page 56   Glossary

page 59   Photographs

EARLY DAYS

I took shape slowly in a tarry shed by the head of the River. My builder's name was Alf and he took great care and pride in seeing that my lines were sweet and shapely. It was just after the War and even Alf had to make do with whatever materials he could get.

My planks were fashioned from larch and elm. My frames were steamed and bent from slender oak lathes. Alf gave my transom a lift above the waterline and shaped it like a wine glass. Finally, when he had finished, he stood back and admired his work. He was well satisfied that I was suited for the task my owners intended to put me.

One day, on the top of the tide, the sailing barge *Joy* came slowly up the River. She belonged to Messrs A N & H Rankin of Rochford in Essex and they had promised her captain, Skipper Moss, a new foot boat.

The mate let go the great anchor with a splash. Skipper Moss put his helm down and the barge rounded up head to tide; she sheered gently into the Quay and they made her fast. Skipper Moss stepped ashore and walked over to the boatyard.

"Have you got my little boat finished yet, Alf?" he asked.

"I have that, Captain," replied Alf. "Come and have a look."

Skipper Moss walked slowly round me. He looked critically at my bold sheer and peered below at my full bilge. He noted my fine run aft and knew that I would leave the water untroubled behind as his mate sculled me. He stood for a long time and read my name JOY   LONDON   cut crisply into my transom.

1

"She'll do fine, Alf," he said at length. "I can see she will row and scull well. I'll take her away just now." And so they rolled me out of that big comfortable shed.

Out from its piles of curly shavings and smells of dark pine forests into the sunlight and out on to the river. They launched me down the slip and into the muddy waters of the Blackwater. Skipper Moss stepped carefully aboard and lifted the heavy oar into my sculling notch. With powerful strokes he drove me up the river until I came alongside what was to be my first home – the sailing barge *Joy*.

The *Joy* was no youngster. She had been built in 1914 in the very same yard as I had been. Her owners were millers and they kept her busy in the grain trade, running from the London River delivering grain to the mills up the Rivers Crouch and Blackwater. She had been in this trade for over forty years before I joined her. Once she was part of a great fleet of barges trading to every little port and forgotten wharf on the East Coast. But now she and her sister the *Lord Roberts* were just two of the handful of barges remaining in trade.

Nevertheless, it was all new and exciting to me. We would sail away up the London River to the docks in search of a freight. Swung high in the davits on the *Joy*'s quarter, I had a fine view of all the busy life of the river. Tugs towing strings of lighters would weave in and out of the traffic. Great steamers from distant countries would snort and blow their sirens angrily as they slowly felt their way up river.

Ugly modern colliers – flatirons we called them – would push half the river ahead of them as they delivered cargoes of coal to the waterside power stations.

Occasionally, we would pass another sailing barge. Skipper Moss always knew her name and seemed to know where she was bound. Through all this traffic the *Joy* would thread her way until we reached our destination.

Sometimes, it was to lay alongside a steamer unloading in the river. Sometimes we would have to go into the docks themselves after our freight. That I did not enjoy. I would spend hours sculling up and down the dock, running off lines so that the Skipper and Mate could heave the barge laboriously to her berth. 'No sailing in the dock' was the rule and it used to make Skipper Moss swear. I would bump and bang between lighters whilst Don the Mate grew hotter and hotter sculling back and forth.

When we got to our ship things did not improve. We would lie alongside and position ourselves carefully so that the elevators could pour out a cascade of grain direct into the *Joy*. Don would shovel away feverishly trying to fill every corner of the hold. The dust would rise in a cloud. I would become smothered and everyone got bad tempered.

But when we locked out and were homeward bound all would be forgotten. Don would throw buckets of water all over the barge and the dust would swill off into the river. He would chuck a bucket or two over me and then wash me out clean. Then with a "Heave ho" I would be slung once more in the davits.

With a sou'westerly wind we would tear down Sea Reach and rush past Southend Pier. Skipper Moss would whistle merrily as he stood at the wheel. Don busied himself over the cabin stove and fine cooking smells came up from the open skylight. If we were lucky we could make the Spitways whilst there was still enough water to slip through. Then we could take the flood tide up the Colne or into the River Blackwater.

I loved the trips up the Blackwater best. It is a large and generous river. Its shores are varied and there was always something new to look at. Sometimes, we would anchor off Bradwell. Don would lower me down into the water with a splash. Then he and Skipper Moss would row up the narrow creek to the old barge hard with its curious twisted posts. They would leave me there lying on my anchor whilst they went for beer at the Green Man. I would wait patiently as the tide came and went silently. I would listen to the call of the curlews and dream of sum-mer voyages. Sometimes, out of cussedness, and if my crew were over long, I would sheer ashore and let the ebbing tide leave me high and dry.

Then when Don finally returned, cheerful and full of beer, he would curse and shout as he tried unsuccessfully to launch me down the mud.

On other trips we would deliver our grain to Messrs Rankins' Mills at Stambridge. Then we would have to wind our way up the narrow River Roach, in between the sea walls. I could not see above them and towed quietly behind the barge.

We would pass Mr Shuttleworth's large black shed at Paglesham. This was where the *Joy* had recently had a big refit and been 'doubled'. This is how bargemen call the practice of nailing a new skin of planks completely over the barges' old and worn out topsides.

Up at the mills they were always pleased to see us. I was much admired and quickly proved myself by winning a sculling race against the *Lord Roberts* boat.

The *Joy* and *Lord Roberts* used to lay together alongside the mill waiting their turn to unload. One summer evening after the tide had ebbed, I was left dreaming astern of the *Joy*, sitting comfortably on the mud. Suddenly, I was awoken by an almighty crash. There was the *Lord Roberts* looking as if a bomb had struck her. Her mast, sprit and sails lay tangled in a heap on deck. Her steering wheel was smashed and all was chaos. I learnt the next day that the fastenings at her stemhead had rusted through and the forestay had broken loose; her gear had crashed down on deck.

Sometimes, when we left Rochford bound light for London, we would go the 'back way' by Havengore Island. Then on the top of the tide the swing bridge serving Foulness Island would open. We would scuttle through out over the Maplins to anchor off Shoeburyness. This was a good shortcut and saved the *Joy* flogging all the way up Swin from the Spitways.

Good days, long days, winter and summer, going about our business with only the winds and tides and our own skills to get us there. The barge did not burn oil and belch smoke. She relied on the forces of nature to earn her living.

But these happy times were soon to come to an end. Trade was dwindling and it was harder and harder to find a freight for an old sailing barge. Finally, the *Joy*'s owners decided her working days were done and that they must sell her. Skipper Moss and his Mate Don would have to be paid off and take their chances elsewhere.

Don had his eye upon another job aboard a bigger coasting ship, but he also had other plans for me. He did a deal with the millers and bought me complete with oars, tholes and anchor. On her last trip in trade down the Blackwater Don jumped aboard me as the barge sailed past Mersea Island. He shipped my oars and cast off from the barge. It was a sad farewell from what had been a happy home.

Don rowed purposefully up the Quarters and so to Mersea Hard. This was to become my new home and the beginning of a new adventure.

MERSEA HACK BOAT

Mersea is an island at the mouth of the River Blackwater. Actually, it is only just an island because it is joined to the rest of England by a long low causeway called The Strood. But the locals are an independent lot and like to think of themselves as a race apart. They are quite right. They are.

Mersea is chiefly famous for two things – Mud and Oysters. I became well acquainted with both these things.

When Don brought me to Mersea he put me to work in the oyster trade. Every morning the smacks would get underway with the clinkety-clink of windlasses and the squeal of rusty blocks. They would slip one after another out of the Quarters. Some would sail down the shore to dredge on the common ground. Others would be away to work their owners' layings up the top of some deserted creek.

When they returned to their moorings I would come alongside. Great sacks of oysters would be dumped aboard me and I would then ferry them ashore. There the oysters would be stored in woven hazel baskets each one holding a 'wash'. The baskets would be kept in pits. The tide flooded through them keeping the oysters alive until they were collected for the market. It was cruel hard work and I became shabby and worn. My fine paintwork was scratched and bruised by the sharp oyster shells. Worst of all were the days 'shramming'.

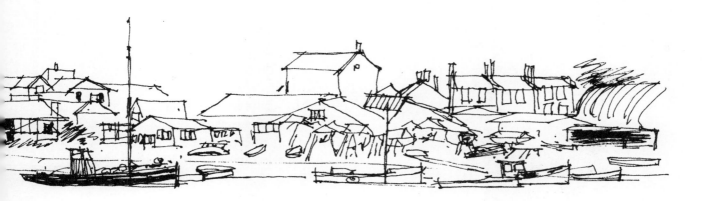

When the oysters spat in the spring they spray out into the water thousands of eggs. If each egg is to grow it must attach itself to a clean sharp piece of shell or stone. In order to provide this, in Mersea's muddy creeks, the oysterman has to cover the bed of his laying with shell and grit. It is called 'shram'. At the top of the Nass spit a freak of the river`s tides casts up a great heap of shram called the Shingle Hills.

On the last of the ebb, I would be rowed off to the Shingle Hills. Two of the oystermen would shovel sandbags full of shram and throw them unceremoniously aboard me. Then,

when I was laden deep in the water, they would row me off to their layings. It was a far cry from those carefree days idling in the *Joy's* davits. I was like a film star reduced to scrubbing doorsteps. My life became a grinding round of toil. It was not that the oystermen neglected me, they merely regarded me as a tool of their trade. Whilst I was fit to do their work I was of use to them. I was allowed one day's rest a week. The smacks did not work on Sundays and I was left swinging to my anchor at the foot of the hard.

I would dream of my days as a barges' boat. Then I was brightly painted and regularly washed clean. Now I was a drab grey

("Nice drop o' crab fat," the smacksman called it as he roughly painted me). Gone were the days when we rushed down Swin cracking on to be home of a Saturday. No longer did a husky barge's mate boast my prowess as a fast rowing boat fit to win any race.

I had not been built for such hard work and it all began to take its toll. My planks became chafed and some of my ribs broke under the cruel sharp sacks of oysters.

My bilges, which were never washed, became filthy and I began to stink. Worst of all I started to leak. This was no use to my masters. They had not time for a leaky boat and so I was left to my fate in a hard berth by the top of the causeway.

For a few pounds I was sold to young Chippy, the greengrocer's son. Chippy had great plans for me but I am sorry to say his ideas outran his abilities. He made a few poor attempts to stop my leaks, became disheartened and abandoned me. My moorings broke. I drove further up the beach and impaled myself upon a stake.

I was a complete wreck!

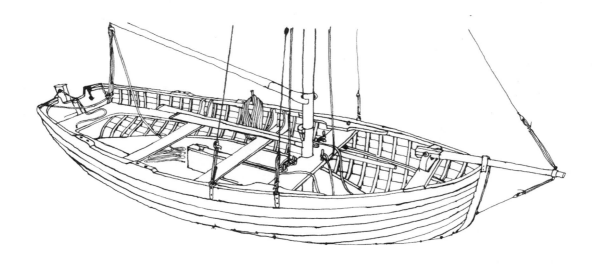

WINKLEBRIG

As my life drained away at the top of Mersea Hard my fate did not go unnoticed.

David was a Mersea boy born and bred. He had been apprenticed to a cabinetmaker and was a skilled carpenter. He saw my sad condition but he also saw my fine lines and admired my shapely transom.

"I could make something of you," he thought and sought out my careless owner. Young Chippy was out drinking beer and David spoke to his father. "Blast the boy," said Old Chippy. "He ain't fit to own a nice little boat like the *Joy*. You come back next week. I will have a word with him and guarantee she will be yours."

This was the longest week of David's life. He had promised to take his wife away on a motoring holiday, but all the time as he drove through the country lanes his mind was elsewhere. He was dreaming of that poor little neglected boat at the top of the Causeway. His wife got quite sharp with him. On the very day he returned to Mersea he raced down to the Hard. With relief he saw that I lay still where he had last seen me – perhaps a little more bruised and battered, he noted gladly. Wasting no time he hurried round to Chippy and bought me for the princely sum of £6.

Never was such a paltry sum better spent.

David lost no time. He loaded me carefully onto a trolley and wheeled me off to his garden. There he set about repairing all my broken planks.

He cut new ribs for me from a fine straight grained piece of rock elm. These were slender lathes 1" x $^3/_4$". Each one had to be steamed in an old drain pipe until it was soft and pliable. Then, whilst the timbers were still hot, David whipped them out of the steam and bent them quickly inside me. Working with speed he drilled each one and secured them with copper rivets. His wife clung on grimly underneath with the dolly whilst David clenched the rivets from within.

Next he cut a slot in my keel and built a centreboard casing. A large and heavy piece of checker plate hinged upon a single bolt to make a lifting keel. This would help me grip the water and sail to windward.

From the builder's yard in the village, David brought a couple of scaffold poles. One he fashioned into a mast topped off by a jaunty cap. The other pole he cut down and made into a boom. The gaff he found for me was an altogether nicer piece of pitch pine. It was light and slender and, when scraped, the clean straight grain came up yellow as a guinea. I was not so pleased with my bowsprit. This was a piece of 1" galvanized water pipe, with an eye welded on the inboard end to fit over my stem head.

The mast was stepped through a new thwart mounted upon my gunwales and set up by a pair of shrouds either side and a forestay to the bowsprit.

The rig looked well proportioned and my spirits soared. At that time David was working during the week at the local football ground. Each night he returned with a van full of timber recovered from the old stadium he was replacing. From this wood he made a close fitting set of floorboards for me. I am now a devoted United supporter.

The final job was to make a rudder. This hung outboard from my transom and had a blade of checker plate which could be raised and lowered.

David now had to find some sails for me. He acquired a high peaked red mainsail of doubtful origin and a rather dingy jib. Above the mainsail he set a topsail on a bamboo jackyard. All the halliards were made fast on a turned row of belaying pins set in the mast thwart.

Come Saturday morning, David wheeled me back down to the Hard. My new paint sparkled in the sun. I floated jauntily in the water with a little red streamer at the masthead.

The transformation was complete. From a tore-out hackboat I had emerged to take my place among the small and exclusive fleet of Mersea winklebrigs.

Let me explain what a winklebrig really is. In those days Mersea still had a thriving oyster industry and the smacks sailed off each day to dredge and cultivate their layings. When they returned, laden deep with oysters, they would be tended by heavy skiffs and rowboats (such

as I had done). Some of the fishermen had rigged their skiffs with a single mast and set a gaff mainsail and a jib to help them ferry the heavy loads ashore. These they called 'bumkins' and often went off dredging in them up the smaller creeks where the smacks found it constricted and difficult to manoeuvre.

The bumkins were a mixed lot. There were in fact some like the *Boy George* who had been especially built for the job, but mostly they had come from different and various backgrounds. Some had served as sprat skiffs and never were built to sail. Others, like me, had been barges' boats or foot boats from sailing trawlers. The prettiest of them all was the *Oyster*, and the *Linda* at Maldon was much admired.

There was the *Jack*, and the *Wheezy Anna*, the *Ma Nabs* and the *Irene*, whilst the *Froggy* had started life aboard a Breton tunneyman. There were some ugly ducklings too. The *Inez* had been an Aldeburgh Beach boat in her youth and was as slow as a church. Nonetheless, her owner defended her qualities staunchly and said she was a fine dredging boat. (I later learned that to be described as 'a fine dredging boat' was the ultimate indignity.) There was the *Winnie*, whose owner was constantly bailing so she was known as the *Weepy Winnie* and the *T D*, sometimes called the *Tedious* –

As the oyster industry fell into decline and ugly motorised dredging platforms replaced the smacks, so too did the bumkins become idle. But not for long. Their sturdy individualism and delightfully simple and adaptable rig had not gone unnoticed.

The bumkins were soon bought up by weekend sailors and amateurs who wanted to pretend they were smacksmen. Every Saturday afternoon you could see a bumkin sailing about the creeks with her proud new owner clad in regulation thigh boats and ex-British Railway waistcoats.

More often than not he would have the peak run off and the tack triced up. It was all part of what is now known as being 'trad'. About the same time everyone dropped the name bumkin and started referring to them as winklebrigs. It sounded much more grand and had a definite ring to it.

No one knew where the name had come from. I, in fact, have my suspicions and reckon we had all had our legs gently pulled.

This, then, was the happy little fleet that I and David joined.

We sailed on summer afternoons up the Ray and he went swimming on the top of the tide. The purple lavender tinged the marsh and the larks cried overhead. We explored the top of Samson's Creek where the bones of the sailing barge *Unity* lay. In springtime we went off in search of gulls' eggs.

It was on one of these trips that I was really able to show my paces. It was a fine May evening. As David set my mainsail we could see another little tan sail way down the creek beyond the packing shed. We gave chase. As we sailed out into the Quarters we saw the *Inez* bear away round Old Hall Point. She was bound for Tollesbury and so were we. "Come on, little *Joy*," urged David, and I hurried on. The owner of the *Inez* glanced astern, saw the gap was narrowing and crouched earnestly over his tiller. With ease we sailed by her and headed up the North Channel. The Skipper of the *Inez* looked black as thunder and pretended not to notice.

We landed on Sunken Island and David stepped ashore. The gulls wheeled and screeched overhead. There lay eggs seemingly scattered at random on the marsh but in fact each was carefully marked by the bird that had laid them. Furiously the gulls swooped and dived as David filled his basket. Back aboard each egg was given the 'floating test'. If an egg floated in a bucket full of water it was fresh, if it sank it was addled – or was it the other way round? Sometimes, David got muddled and went home with a feed of rotten eggs.

When David had his fill we were off again. There was the *Inez* just sailing by the smacks anchored at the Leavins. "If we hurry, little *Joy*," said David, "We will get her again." And so we did. We slipped through the *Inez*'s lee, rounded up at Rickers and passed her on the way back. Her owner, Charles, said nothing and looked even blacker.

Little did I know it but I was to come across that young man again.

They were happy times and David took good care of me but it was not long before he began to cast his eyes longingly at the few smacks that remained in the creek. He became ambitious and decided he must move on from a humble winklebrig and buy a proper ship.

It was not long before David was able to buy his smack and I found myself once again laid up by the causeway awaiting a buyer.

THE FLEET

I did not have long to wait.

There was, living in Mersea then, a young widow called Janet. She had two small children, Ben and Sallie, and a crossbred lurcher dog called Stormy. Janet knew about winklebrigs and had in fact sailed the *Linda* out of Maldon on many occasions.

She owned a handsome black Baltic Trader called the *Solvig* and was in the charter business.

Every Friday night an excited group of passengers would come to the foot of the causeway and have to be ferried off aboard the *Solvig*. Janet needed an extra boat to help with this work. She also wanted a little boat to teach Ben and Sallie how to sail. She thought, quite rightly, that I would be ideal for both these jobs.

A bargain was struck and David sold me to Janet complete with a mooring in the Gut and a dreadful little dinghy which tipped you over the side the moment you set foot in her.

I enjoyed my new work. Janet handled me with sympathy and understanding. She was a skilled sailor and I always gave her my best.

The *Solvig*'s passengers would crowd aboard and I would be loaded to the gunwales with gear. They would all be chattering and laughing excitedly looking forward to their week's holiday. I would thread my way through the moorings out to the Quarters. The *Solvig* lay off the end of Old Hall Point and I would luff alongside. Rodney the Skipper would catch my painter and the passengers would scramble up aboard. Then it would be back in the growing darkness for another load. Finally when they were all safely aboard the *Solvig* I would be returned to my comfortable mooring in the Gut.

On Sundays, I would take Janet, Ben and Sallie and Stormy sailing. The children learned fast and soon became confident. It was not long before they both could sail me without their mother's help. She had the sense to let them get on with it and trusted me to see that they came to no harm.

Stormy the lurcher was the fourth member of the crew. He would stand up forrard with his forepaws over the stem head, ears streaming in the wind. He was a proper sea dog and had impeccable references. He was born in a gale of wind off the Suffolk coast aboard the sailing barge *Cambria*. Janet always described him as a Suffolk Barge hound when anyone enquired about his breeding.

He grew up on the coast and spent his early days running back and forth to London on various barges. When his master, Peter, settled on the Blackwater, Stormy became well known on the river. He would fight any dog twice his size and was a regular terror for the ladies. He was once seen climbing up a drainpipe to get to one particular poodle bitch. His great pleasure was trawling. When the cod-end was emptied across the deck, Stormy would chase the crabs to their hiding places barking and stamping with his forepaws. Then he would worry away at them until they nipped his nose or he was able to put them to rest with a crunch.

But now Stormy was growing old. His muzzle had gone grey and his eyes were turning rheumy. Nevertheless, he enjoyed his days sailing with me and would sniff the breeze and dream of his time barging.

But it wasn't all idling about. I have a fair turn of speed and Janet was keen to go racing. She decided we should enter the Maldon Regatta Race for Fisherman's Open Boats. After all Maldon was the place of my birth, what better than to return and show them all how fast and agile I was in my new rig? I was given a fresh coat of paint; my bottom was scrubbed clean and painted bright red with anti-fouling. Off we set for Maldon Quay.

Race Day was bright and sharp. There was a fresh breeze from the south west. With Janet at the helm and Ben and Sallie as crew we came to the starting line. The gun boomed and we were off. It was a tight sheet to the weather mark off Mill Beach. Soon we drew out ahead. Astern came the *Linda* followed by the *Torment*. I revelled in it and lay to the breeze, nearly dipping my lee rail under. We rounded the big red buoy off the tip of Northey Island. Janet slacked off the main sheet and Ben eased my jib. We tore home to cross the finishing line way ahead of our rivals. That night there was much singing and merrymaking at the Jolly Sailor. I lay quietly alongside the Quay, content, knowing that I had returned home and covered myself with glory.

At the prize giving ceremony, Janet collected a large cup and kindly old Sammy, the Commodore, presented Ben and Sallie each with a special prize "for the youngest crew in the race."

And so the summer passed, autumn turned to winter and the days grew shorter. Janet laid me up and put me to rest in a comfortable mudberth at the foot of the Lane. Christmas brought frosts and there was for a time ice on the muds. This can be dangerous to little wooden boats like me if we are left in the tideway. The ice is as sharp as razor blades and as it moves on the tide it can cut and scar the bows of a boat. But I was safe and although the snow covered me in a white mantle, I took no harm.

Next spring came late but it brought with it a new person in my life.

There was at that time a fishing smack call the *Iris* on the top of the slipway. Her owner, Charles, had moved on from his winklebrig *Inez* to a smack. He had been working hard on her, replacing her rotten stem and worn out planks. Janet would go and watch the work progressing and encourage the amateur shipwright. When the day's work was done they would both go back to Janet's warm and cosy cottage at the top of the Lane in Mersea.

By the time the *Iris* was finished and ready to be launched again, Janet and her owner had decided to get married. That summer I was part of this happy fleet. The *Solvig* was the Queen, the *Iris* the family boat and I was the humble little workhorse fetching and carrying passengers.

However, my time was to come. One day a man came to Janet's cottage. "They are making a film round Walton Backwaters, and they urgently need a sailing boat," he said. "Would you charter the *Joy*?"

"Tell me more about it," asked Janet.

"The film is based upon the book by Paul Gallico called 'The Snow Goose'," he said. "It is a lovely story all about a lonely man who lives by a marsh. His only friend is a goose who he has trained to come to his call. He owns a little sailing boat and the *Joy* would be ideal."

Janet agreed. However, she was reluctant to give me to the film company without someone taking proper care of me. One day the film stars came down to Mersea and Janet took them off for a sail in me. The leading lady, who was beautiful and intelligent, was sympathetic and quickly learned to take my tiller. However, the hero of the film just could not understand the limitations of a sailing boat. He sensed he was out of his element and resented being shown how to do something. He quickly lost interest and relapsed into silence.

I was loaded on to a lorry and bumped away to Walton Backwaters. Here for two weeks I was really the star of the show. The hero never did learn how to sail me and a Mersea fisherman had to lie unseen upon my floorboards, his hand upon the tiller, as the hero sailed me off into the sunset.

I am very proud of my role as a star. The film has become a classic and is still shown on the television.

That year we went racing again – or rather we did not! Janet entered the *Solvig*, the *Iris* and myself, the *Joy*, in the East Coast Old Gaffers' Race. This is a very important event. Nearly a hundred old boats gather up the River and set sail in a great armada out to the sea. It is a fine sight and the river is filled with a patchwork of tanned sails.

It was another hard and windy race day and Janet quite wisely refused to put me at risk. Instead we blew up the river and spent the day quietly on the beach at Osea Island.

Not so the *Solvig*. Her Skipper, Dudley, raced off down the River. She was the biggest ship in the race that year and honour was at stake. She did well and led the fleet home.

That night Dudley stepped forward to receive his prize. "You might as well take the *Joy*'s prize with you," said the harassed Secretary. "She was first in the open boat class." Dudley, who did not know I had not even taken part in the race, did as he was asked and took the cup as well. In the confusion, out of a hundred vessels racing, some other unfortunate winner had been mistaken for the *Joy*.

Thus, I became the only winkle-brig to win the Old Gaffers' Race without actually crossing the starting line!

But soon all these happy days on the Blackwater were to come to an end and I was to become a wanderer again.

SCOTLAND

Charles had gone to work in Scotland and he wanted his family and the *Joy* to come too.

There can be few more ignominious ways for a winklebrig to travel than to be carted aboard a sheep wagon.

I mean to say, after swinging in splendour from a barge's davits, tearing up and down Swin, to be heaved and pushed up the tailboard of a large and gloomy wagon below a deck of sheep – the smell! not to mention all the other horrors which fell from the load above.

I endured the long journey in silence and resented being torn from my beloved river. At long last we arrived. I was dragged from my foetid berth and launched upon a cruel hard coast – the Solway Firth.

Janet and Charles had found a new home for me upon the river Urr at Kipford. I will admit it was all very beautiful. The river wound its way between pine clad hills to the little granite town of Dalbeattie. But its banks were steep and unfriendly. The tide rushed back and forth cutting deep scars in the sand. As the tide ebbed it would carve a new course and the banks would fall with a crash. The sand which looked firm was treacherous and would swallow anything that fell into the river. Nevertheless, I am not one to sulk and I decided to make the best of a bad job. I put a brave face on things and we set about exploring this new country.

We searched for its history and the ships that had once traded here. There was nothing left. Once upon a time the schooners had sailed up the Urr. They took granite setts from the quarries away to Liverpool and returned with cattle feed. Sometimes it was pit props for the mines in England and back with coals for the riverside villages. But unlike the barges in my home country, all these schooners had disappeared long ago.

They had been built at Kipford but now there was only a boring fleet of modern yachts. No one seemed interested in what had gone before. The yachtsmen barely noticed me as I turned nimbly through their moorings.

That first winter in Scotland Charles took me in pursuit of wildfowl out upon the Solway. He lashed a large muzzle loading punt gun upon my bows. We would take the ebb out of Kipford and sail out beyond Heston. There we would find great rafts of ducks and geese sitting upon the water. We would place ourselves upwind of them and then sail down silently and as swiftly as we could upon the sleeping ducks. My crew would be hidden low upon the floorboards out of sight, one at the helm and the other crouched up forrard behind the big gun. As we approached the fowl they would waken and start to swim away from me. Sometimes they would misjudge my speed and we could approach near enough for a shot. Then the gunner would wave his arm, the duck would spring from the water, and the gun would roar over my bows. A sheet of flame and a cloud of smoke would roll ahead of me and wads of burning oakum would scatter the water. Sometimes there would be the wretched corpses of a few unlucky duck to retrieve. More often, there was nothing. I was secretly relieved when the duck escaped. I resented the slaughter of such beautiful birds. Actually, I could upset the gunner's aim and would try at the crucial moment to raise and plunge my bows so that the shot went wide.

After Christmas I was laid up in the Saltings. Janet and her family decided they would find a new mooring for me nearer their home.

This was a disastrous decision and was very nearly the death of me!

SWALLOWED BY THE QUICKSANDS

Further east upon the shores of the Solway, the mountain Criffel rises steeply. At its foot, where the River Nith joins the Solway, there is a little village. The great red sandstone ruin of Sweetheart Abbey stands high above the whitewashed granite cottages.

Built in the twelfth century by Sir John Balliol it was named after his wife Devorgilla. All the sandstone was ferried by ship from across the Nith up a winding creek called the Pow. Later, much later, a quay was built to serve the village at the head of the Pow. It was called Bog Quay and had been a busy place. Once upon a time a narrow railway brought granite from the quarry high up the slopes of Criffel. Timber from the forests went away south from Bog Quay and the schooners returned with coals for the village. But now all had fallen into decay. Brambles grew over the quay and its walls bulged. The creek had become silted and trees grew close by its banks. Winter gales had torn great branches down and their gaunt limbs lay rearing from the creek like prehistoric monsters. It was a gloomy place. The Pow

25

emptied out into the shallow Solway and came adry three hours before low water. Still, there was a little pool at the mouth and it was here that Charles had laid a mooring for me. Jocky, a kindly farmer, had said that Janet could drive through his farm to get there. It was close to their new home and it would be more convenient. That is what they thought at least!

That April I bid farewell to the river Urr with little regret. It was a bright blustery morning when, with Jocky aboard, we set sail. Passing Heston Island we stood out into the Solway. Away to windward the surf curled upon the Barnhourie Sands. Ashore, Criffel rose high above us and the larch forest was just coming green.

Off Southerness Light the wind increased. I crashed through the short seas and occasionally the spray broke aboard. Jocky became silent and turned faintly green. He grasped my gunwale and his knuckles showed white. Charles at the helm was oblivious of his crew's discomfort and was confident of my ability to weather the Ness. Soon Carsethorn was abeam and the sea became calmer. The centre plate was raised and we scuttled in across the shallow water.

Janet, Ben and Sallie and of course Stormy were waiting at the mouth of the Pow to welcome us. I rounded up into the wind and ran gently ashore at my new mooring. Jocky leapt ashore. "Och mon, I've niver been so worrit in mae life!" he said and dashed off to the safety of his farmhouse.

I was the only boat on the Pow (that should have said something!), but we sailed that summer, venturing up the Nith and out into the Solway.

We never saw any other boats and my only companions at the Pow were the Haaf-net fishers. In the early summer the salmon run up the Solway heading for the fresh water rivers and their spawning ground. Higher up the Nith at Dumfries they could be seen leaping up the Caul. The Haaf-net fishers were a secretive lot. Their licences to fish the salmon were jealously guarded and passed only upon death to a close friend or a member of their families. By day they worked upon the farms or in the village saw mills, but in the summer evenings they would be 'away to the fishing'. Each man carried his own net. Some 10' wide by 5' deep at one end, it tapered to 2' at the other. The net was bent to a wooden frame with a handle upon the upper bar.

As the tide started to flood up the
channel the fishers would stand in a
line from the shore to the centre of
the water. They would lean forward
upon their net with a corner of it
linked to their fingers. Then, as the
salmon swimming upon the incoming
tide struck the net the men would
scoop them up with a sweeping
movement. Then it was thud! crash!
splash! with a little short cudgel,
called a priest, and the salmon would

be slung into a sack behind the fishers' shoulders. Each man wore long waders up to his
armpits. As the tide rose the man in the deep water near the centre of the creek would move
inshore so the order in the line was constantly changing. One day we sat and watched them
for hours.

The fishers were suspicious and hostile. Perhaps they thought I had an income tax inspector
aboard! You see the fishers always swore it was the worst season on record and the salmon
just were not there.

One day, Janet asked in the village shop if it was possible to buy a salmon. "Och I see what
my man can do," was the reply. That night no less than three fishers called after dark with
soggy bulging sacks offering to sell Janet salmon.

After a time even the fishers softened and we would often watch them and pass a summer's
evening with them. The old boy, who always kept his fags dry under his cap, was the cheeri-
est. I noticed that summer he bought himself a brand new motor car!

Winter came early that year. By November the leaves had all been torn from the beeches in
Shambellie Forest. The heavy rains filled the burns high on Criffel. Brown with peat and
swollen, the torrents raced downhill to discharge into the Pow. I tugged fretfully at my
mooring at the mouth of the creek.

One night as the tide rose there came a great wind driving on shore. The short steep waves met the fresh water pouring down the Pow.

My bilges were full of rainwater too and I pitched and tossed heavily in the darkness. The storm increased and on the top of the tide my mooring rope was fouled by floatsam sweeping out to sea. My bows were pinned down. I could not rise to the waves. In an instant I was swamped and sank beneath the flow to rest upon the bed of the creek.

Next morning, Jocky, who was tending his cattle, saw my mast poking drunkenly above the rushing fresh water. Weed festooned my rigging and a dead sheep swirled past.

He could do nothing to help me but telephoned Janet with the bad news. That evening they came to my aid but by then it was too late!

The shifting, moving, sands had even then grasped hold of me and had started to swallow me up. I was fixed fast and immovable. The water never left me because of the rains and all they could do was cut my riggings and salvage my mast and spars. "We'll get her when the fresh abates," said Charles. But it rained and rained and the water never left me until the spring. Then, at last, when the creek was dry, they returned. The channel had shifted and the quicksand had done its work. There was nothing left to show my grave except the tail of my mooring rope.

Janet and her family tried to dig me free.

It was cruel work. The sand was tenacious and would not leave their shovels. Worse still the hole filled with water. They worked four feet down the rope and probed with rods another fathom – nothing – there was no sign of me.

At last even Janet had to admit I was lost. How tantalising! She knew the exact position of my grave, but the Solway sand was unyielding and kept me hidden.

For six long years I lay there, slumbering and stifled beneath the Solway, just another wreck upon that treacherous coast.

"………… LIKE APHRODITE"

The telephone rang. It was Jocky. "Janet, I do believe the *Joy* is uncovered," he said. "I was away to the fishing last night, and I could see her outline in the bed of the creek. I do believe we could get her."

They lost no time. Gathering together ropes and chains and a quantity of forty gallon drums, Janet and her family set off for the Pow. She even impressed some friends from Glasgow, who had travelled south for Sunday lunch, to help her.

When they reached the creek they saw to their delight the sands had shifted. There in the bottom of the creek, level with the bottom, was my outline. Everyone set to digging out the sand from within me. If only that could be cleared and the barrels lashed inside me the rising tide might just lift me from my grave. Feverishly they dug, racing against time. By evening most of the sand was cleared from within me. Janet and Charles were able to slip chains under my keel and so secure the barrels within, that they might lift me as they floated. At last there was nothing further they could do. Cold and exhausted, plastered with mud from top to toe, the little party walked back up to Jock's farmhouse to wait for the midnight tide.

It was a full moon that night. Charles returned just before high water. The creek was full of silvery water and there, floating in the centre, was my half submerged form hanging from the barrels. Gently, hardly daring to breathe, he pulled the sullen mass ashore, and there on the beach I grounded softly, raised like the Goddess of the Sea herself. He sat by me in the moonlight that night as the tide left me, wondering at my luck. The Solway does not often yield up her dead but she had released me.

Next day they loaded me onto a wagon and took me up to the farm. Jocky had a pressure hose, with which they loosened the remaining sand in my bilges. All sorts of familiar objects were revealed. Janet's slippers still tucked beneath a thwart and Charles's favourite pipe lodged behind my stringer came to view.

I had really taken little harm during my long years in the sand. Less harm in fact than comes of neglecting a little clinker-built boat upon the dry land.

Janet promised me a real refit and took me off to an airy barn on their small farm. All that summer Charles worked away upon me, making new floorboards, burning off my perished paint work and patching up my rotting transom.

I shared the barn with Sallie's ponies. She had a pretty little grey mare called Spring. Spring had given birth that year to a boisterous colt foal called Falcon. In addition to these two there was a crabbet little coloured pony named Pan and a big lumpy Irish van horse called Flint. Flint was big and friendly, even if he was a little stupid. He used to lean his head over the gate; his lower lip would hang loose and quiver slightly as he dozed on his feet.

It was Falcon who really got on my nerves. He was restless and spiteful and would nip Flint's broad quarters when he was not looking. I ignored Falcon and preserved a stony silence. But one night Falcon had his revenge. He stretched across the rail into my stall and started to gnaw away at my gunwale.

By morning he had chewed a great ragged hole in me. Janet was furious and Charles threatened to send Falcon off to the knackers. Sallie wisely hurried all the horses off out of sight to the other end of the farm and let things cool down. I mean to say that wretched horse had done more damage to me than six years beneath the Solway.

HOME AGAIN

"I am never going to launch the *Joy* upon the Solway again," said Janet. "It is no place for an elderly brig." "Quite so," said Charles "Let's take her back to Mersea."

So off I went again upon my travels, but this time it was a merry little brig that travelled south down the motorway. Imagine my pleasure as we crossed the Strood and once again I came to Mersea Island. They unloaded me upon the Hard and set about rigging me there. Old friends stopped to yarn as they walked down to the water. "God Blast Alive," said one fisherman. "If that ain't the *Joy*! I had heard she was lost in Scotland. I was mate once in the barge *Joy* and have sculled that boat miles." David, too, came to see the little boat he had once rescued and also John, the shipwright. He brought caulking cotton and putty and set about staunching a bad leak around my centre plate box.

Once again Janet and I sailed the Blackwater. We spent lazy summer days up at the Golden Strand. The big midday tides filled the saltings until only the sea lavender showed purple above the water.

At Heybridge Basin we joined the Regatta and chased round the buoys. I picked up my heels and tried to keep up with the rest of the Fisherman's Open boats. To tell the truth, it was in vain. These days they rig the brigs up like J class yachts. Great towering masts and clouds of sail. Their crews hang from trapezes and they have a pump in either bilge. "Painted Huzzys," I thought. "I bet it is a long time since you set off for a days oystering or winkling." It seems a shame to me to take an honest working boat and turn her into a racing machine.

Still, it was a happy homecoming and I felt at ease and among friends. Finally, their holiday done, Janet and Charles took me up to Peldon and made me secure in that little muddy haven for smacks and workboats that John the shipwright had created. He would keep an eye on me because Janet and her family were to start upon a new chapter in their lives. It was to be a chapter in which for a time I was to play no part.

OLD FRIENDS

Janet and her family moved south from Scotland to far-off Cornwall. Here they made a new life for themselves. They found a little oyster dredger called the *Shamrock* lying neglected in a muddy creek overhung by oak trees. She had been employed upon the Fal Oyster Fishery but her skipper had died. Now his family was trying to sell her.

They drove a hard Cornish bargain, but before long the *Shamrock* was loaded on to a lorry and transported to Janet's shed to be repaired.

This was to take two years.

I lay patiently at Peldon – neglected, yes, but happy with my own thoughts. In the winter I was joined by other fishing smacks. On Sundays their owners would come aboard and light their cabin stoves and drink tea. The coal smoke and sparks from the chimneys would drift across the creek. In the spring, all was bustle and activity. Blowlamps would flare and scrapers squeal as old paint was removed. There would be sawing and hammering and the smell of freshly cut oak. Then out would come the paint pots and the smacks would sparkle. Masts would be scraped and varnished until they winked butter yellow in the sun. Heavy red mainsails would be lugged aboard across the swaying gang planks. Blocks and running rigging would be sent aloft. And then when all was ready and the spring tides filled the creek, the smacks would set their sails and slip away, one by one, down to the river and their various summer moorings.

Once again I would be left alone. There were of course the ghosts of the *Solvig* and the *Iris* to keep me company. Poor ships. Both had once spent their winters safely berthed at Peldon, but now they were gone.

The *Solvig* left her bones upon the rocky shores of Ibiza in the Mediterranean. One night a storm blew up. What had been a sheltered anchorage suddenly became exposed and dangerous. Her anchor chain parted and she was driven towards the shore. Her drowsy crew tried in vain to start her big semi-diesel engine. This was a vast twin cylinder contraption with a fly wheel that weighed a ton. You had to heat the cylinder heads with gas torches for ten minutes, then give a squirt of compressed air to turn the engine over. If you were lucky she fired and the flywheel spun the right way. Then, with a reassuring thump, thump, thump you were off, smoke rings blowing from the bent exhaust. Alas, that night the engine failed and the *Solvig* was dashed against the rocks. By morning she was pounded to firewood and in a week all was gone.

The *Iris's* end was even sadder. When our little fleet was sold she went to France. Her new owner voyaged south through the Bay of Biscay to the Mediterranean. After spending time there they sailed on south along the shores of Africa. Then turning her head to the west, they set about crossing the Atlantic Ocean to South America. The plucky little oyster dredger who had spent over half a century on the Blackwater rode the big Atlantic rollers like a gull.

"When the wind was too strong for sailing," said the Frenchman, "I would go below, close the hatch and make love to my girl." OH LA LA!! Finally, strained and leaking the brave *Iris* fetched up in Recife in Brazil. After some rudimentary repairs she sailed north to the Caribbean and so made the circle home once again to Brittany. It was a remarkable voyage. After that she had an extensive refit. No expense was spared and she emerged from the Breton Ship yard strong and good as new. Then she set sail back to her old haunts and came to Brightlingsea at the mouth of the River Colne. Here she received a brand new mainsail from James the Master Sailmaker. She set off down to the north to circumnavigate the British Isles. Sallie, now grown to an adventurous girl of thirteen, went too. Skirting the Wash they headed north. They passed the Humber and Flamborough Head following the old Colliers' route.

First the Dudgeon then the Spurn
Flamborough Head come next in turn
Filey Brigg as you pass by
Whitby light bear northerly

But then their luck ran out. North of Hartlepool one night, they were becalmed. The Frenchman was exhausted after being so long at sea. His crew was only two teenage girls and they all slept. The *Iris* became embayed and was set ashore upon a desolate place called Blackhall Rocks. Next day the wind backed and came easterly. Upon the rising ride the swell lifted her and pounded her mercilessly.

A sea swept her hatches and filled her hold. She burst asunder and spewed her contents upon the shore. Then the tide receded and left the poor battered *Iris* on the beach. That night the wreckers came creeping down the cliff path. The Frenchman and Charles, who had come to help, fought them in vain. They were outnumbered and had to withdraw bruised and bloody.

The wreckers poured petrol on the *Iris* and set fire to her. All they wanted was her iron ballast and copper fastenings. Next morning only a pile of ash remained to wash away upon the incoming tide.

That is how the *Iris* died.

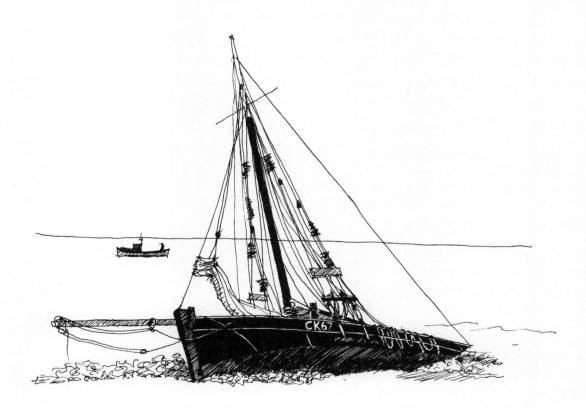

CORNWALL AND THE RIVER FAL

So I lay at Peldon all alone. I grew shabby and started to feel my age. My paintwork cracked and peeled. The weather lifted the varnish-work on my spars and they became dull. Rainwater and mud filled my bilges. Small crabs scuttled beneath my floorboards. They must have been carried there as spawn in the leaking saltwater. Soon they grew large.
But then one winter's day I was awoken. A fussy little motor boat took me in tow and led me off down the winding creek past the Ray and so to Mersea Hard. There, waiting for me, was a large Land Rover with a trailer all ready to carry me off once again.
We made the long journey across England to the west passing through strange inland towns where a brig has never passed before. Oxford, Cheltenham and then on to Bristol. Finally, we drove down deep and narrow lanes to Janet's new home in Cornwall.

"Poor little *Joy*," said Janet when she saw me. "We have neglected you. What a state you are in. It is a wonder you did not rattle to bits down the motorway and leave a trail of copper fastenings behind you."

They lost no time in setting about me. I was washed out thoroughly and all the Essex crabs cleaned from my bilges. Then I was rolled inside a large dry barn. It was quite clear that I needed extensive repairs. My stem was rotten and loose, many of my ribs were cracked and at least two planks would have to be replaced. They also decided to renew all my thwarts which were distinctly shabby.

The first job was to secure the planking at my bows. A piece of oak called an apron fitted right up behind my stem reaching from the gunwale right down to the upper side of the keel. All the plank ends were fastened to this with brass screws. Then the old and rotten stem was removed, and the ragged plank ends trimmed off flush with the forrard edge of the new apron. Now a new curved stem could be fitted and secured with long bolts to the apron.

Next they set about fashioning new ribs for me. These were made from straight grained oak laths 1" x ³/₄". In order for them to be bent around the sharp turn of my bilge they had to be made supple and pliant. To do this they had to be boiled and steamed. Charles got a length of steel tubing 4" in diameter. One end was welded up and made watertight. The pipe was lagged with old sacking and part filled with water. The lathes were then boiled in this long kettle until they were quite soft. Then, wearing heavy gloves because they were so hot,

Charles would quickly draw one out and bend it immediately within me so it followed my shape from gunwale to gunwale. Each rib was secured with copper nails through the overlapped planks. Janet lay underneath holding the dolly whilst Charles hammered on the rivets' heads from within.

Slowly I began to recover my self respect and strenth. The barn became full of curly shavings and reminded me of that tarry shed long ago where I first took shape.

I felt that my builder Alf was looking on. He was pleased that someone still cared about his handiwork, even though he shuddered sometimes at their clumsy efforts to restore me.

Every other weekend Janet and Charles would travel south to Fowey to collect more wood for me. They would cross the deep river there in the ferryboat and go to the shipyard upon the Polruan Shore. Here they built great wooden fishing boats. The vast shed was filled with the hum of woodworking machinery. Shipwrights swung their adzes and sent the chips of oak flying.

It seemed incongruous to interrupt all this activity for a footling little order for a winklebrig. But the proprietor of the yard was a friendly person and took time and care to attend to them. "There, that will keep you out of mischief for a week," he would say as they left the yard carrying a bundle of bright new wood between them.

New thwarts from hard yellow iroko were shaped and fitted. A complete new top strake of mahogany was wrapped around my port side. A fine new bowsprit replaced the ugly iron spike I used to have.

Soon all that was left to be done was to give me a complete paint up. Bright red floorboards, and light blue inside, thwarts and topside a matching turquoise all set off by a navy blue top-strake.

How smart and proud I felt as I was wheeled out into the spring sunshine ready to explore my new Cornish home.

THE CREEK WHERE TIME STANDS STILL

Midway up the Fal, above the Ferry, the River widens and forms a large 'S' bend. Here it is joined by two narrow winding creeks, which merge and empty into it. At this place is a large granite capped quay. This was to be my new home.

Once upon a time it had been a busy place. Trains of packhorses would pick their way slowly down a rutted track laden with minerals from the mines away inland. Schooners and brigs lay alongside waiting to load. There was a counting house where dues were paid and a boat-builders' yard too.

But now it was a quiet and peaceful place. Birches and gorse bushes grew where the horses' hooves had clattered over the cobbles. The roof was off the counting house and only the four walls remained. Great oak and beech trees covered the hill behind and hid a mysterious ancient earthworks.

The creek winds between steep banks. They are covered with old untidy plum orchards which fall right down to the water's edge. In spring, daffodils grow beneath the trees and ewes call to their lambs.

Small stone cottages are built into the hillside and on calm evenings the smoke rises up, lazily, from their chimneys. Old neglected slipways covered in weed serve each cottage, and oyster-men's punts swing on their moorings. This was a place where the inhabitants lived with one foot on the land and one foot in the water.

In winter they were busy gathering oysters from the River fishery to place upon their own layings in the creek. Crooked withies marked each patch and these were very jealously guarded. Here the oysters would grow fatter until they were ready to be marketed.

In order to preserve the stocks of oysters in the River and the Harbour, it is a rule that no engines may be used to fish the oysters. The only way they may be caught is from a sailing boat, or a hand hauled punt, or by simply walking along the beach, at low tide and picking up what you may find.

My new companion the *Shamrock* had been engaged upon this Fishery for forty years and had worked all that time from my new home.

In the summer the inhabitants tended their gardens and their orchards. The trees would become laden with little blue plums, sharp and bitter to the taste, but make them into jam and they are transformed into nectar.

The other local industry was tending the ships which came to lay up in the River. In times of depression and slack trade, the River would be full of rusting unemployed shipping. They filled the narrow River like sleeping monsters. Each ship had to be moored up securely to enormous buoys. The tugs would come up from the Harbour towing a ship. The men from the creek would meet them and take charge. With great skill they would manoeuvre them into position and make all fast. The work was then not over because each ship had to have a watchman and each watchman had to be relieved.

The ships were brought straight out of trade, some destined only for the breakers. They were crammed full of all manner of gear! There was never any shortage of paint and heavy tackle in our little creek.

It took a long time for me to get to know the inhabitants of my new home. They were a secretive lot, rightly jealous of the unspoiled beauty of their creek.

I was on my best behaviour, kept myself smart and tidy and bothered no one. We sailed up and down the creek, Janet skillfully tacking me in the fickle winds that either funnel up or down. I was aware that we were under silent observation and I was anxious to acquit myself well.

It was the Admiral who broke the ice. He was a tall kindly man with a trimmed grey beard. He and his wife lived in the prettiest cottage overlooking my mooring. At the water's edge he had a boatshed crammed to bursting with all manner of gear culled over the years from the sea. Each morning, winter and summer, I would watch him walk down the narrow steps from his cottage to swim in the murky waters of the creek. Then he would row his punt, with strong powerful strokes, off up the River to inspect the tide line.

One day when Janet and Charles were sitting idly aboard, the Admiral rowed off from his cottage towards us. As he approached he paused and laid upon his oars. "I have a picture here which will interest you," he said.

He handed over a large and faded sepia photograph in an oak frame.

It was Rochford Mills, fifty years ago, with the barges *Joy* and *Lord Roberts* laying alongside, and there alongside was ME, a young barges' boat fresh from the builders'. Long ago the Admiral had grown up in Essex and watched the barges come and go up the Crouch. After that we became firm friends and it was comforting to know that there was a watchful eye keeping a look over me.

At the head of the creek the twentieth century rubbed uneasy shoulders with the waterside. Here the cottages had been 'discovered' and become 'desirable riverside homes'. One had been turned into a studio and from here its owner kept her beady eye upon the life of the creek. Her garden was immaculate and she fought a constant battle with her neighbours' straying sheep. They finally broke through and trampled across the tidy flowerbeds. The peace of the creek was shattered with unladylike oaths. On occasions, she would come sailing with Janet aboard me. This was always fun with much wine and much laughter. Across the creek lived Guinness. He was a large woolly Alsatian who went off each night in a white Land Rover with his owner on security duties. What kind of job Guinness made of this I do not know for he was really a great big softy. Once when I was lying on the beach being painted, Guinness hopped aboard and curled up for a sleep in the afternoon sun. He left behind a lot of large muddy paw marks and a hairy patch upon the fresh paint.

THE SECRET RIVER

Further up the Fal and upon the other shore is a mysterious and secret River. It became one of my most favourite places and we often sailed quite alone upon its waters.

Many years ago it was much deeper and large ships sailed far inland to carry cargoes to and from its quays. But then the china clay industry grew above its source. Chalky white waste from the mines washed into the Secret River. Its course became choked, its quays were silted up and became unapproachable.

The ships no longer came and the brickworks with its tall chimney closed down. Now it was quite deserted and drained dry at low water. When the young flood tide first returned we would sail up with it.

The River wound and twisted through woods of oak. Upon the port hand side the trees gave way to a great park and often deer could be seen grazing.

On the other shore the herons made their untidy nests in the spring, and in the dark waters below bass and mullet would swim. Their spiny fins would break the surface and away they would go leaving a sharp wake as I sailed by. You can see no houses from the Secret River. Its banks are cloaked with trees and only occasionally do you get a further view of the folded Cornish countryside.

On summer evenings, Janet and her friends would sail me off up the Secret River to her Picnic Beach. I would be laden with good food and many bottles of wine. I would land upon a small sandy beach where an old track led away through the steep woods to the nearest village.

Everyone would splash ashore chattering merrily and I would be pushed off into the tide to swing upon my anchor. Dry leaves and sticks would be gathered for a fire and soon the acrid wood smoke would blow across the creek, to be followed by the tantalising smells of grilling steaks.

Feasting and partying would go on long after dark. Sometimes there would be music, but it seemed a shame to break the silence of the woods. Then at last when the tide had turned it would be time to drift slowly home. The moon would rise above the trees and the River would shine like polished pewter below. They would row me down to the Fal where the glaring lights from the pub ashore looked harsh and garish after the soft darkness of the Secret River. I would slip quietly up to my mooring by the silent quay, a happy and contended brig.

Other summer evenings were spent fishing. The mullet and the bass love the warm muddy creeks. Mullet feed upon the weeds and make distinctive little marks in the mud. Bass are carnivores and fill their bellies with soft crabs and shrimps. Charles had a large gill net which stowed neatly in a bin which fitted between my thwarts. When all this was loaded aboard, we would set off on the flooding tide to a likely-looking creek. Upon the high water, the net would be strung from shore to shore, effectively cutting off all escape. Now we would wait as the tide drained away. At first nothing happened, but then as the creek emptied there would be swirlings and splashings. Fins would come streaking down the edges and hit the net. The entangled fish would slap and splash but the net was lethal and not many escaped.

Occasionally, a bass would leap like a salmon and clear the net and get away to the sea.

Then before all the water had left the creek we would haul. An old sack would be draped over my gunwale to stop the net snagging. Hand over hand the net would be hauled aboard. If we were lucky there would be a heap of mullet and bass lying on my floorboards. Laden deep we would sail back and go alongside the *Shamrock*. Here the long laborious job of 'shaking out' took place. The net would be hauled, spread wide across the *Shamrock*'s bulwarks. Each fish had to be untangled, one by one. The little soft green crabs had to be cleared from the net and all the mass of twigs and leaves shaken out. It was a messy business and I was glad when it was all over.

The fish scales clung to my paintwork for weeks after. Actually, Charles was rather proud of these and never washed them all away. He felt it proved his prowess as a fisherman!!

In winter the Secret River was even more mysterious. We scavenged its banks for firewood. The chain-saw would snap and snarl and the sawdust would fly. Soon I would be loaded deep with great slabs of sharp smelling oak. Then ponderously and slowly I would sail home feeling like a pregnant cow. Once they made me tow a great log astern, but I jibbed at that and sullenly refused to come about just as they were shaping to pick my mooring up. I was secretly pleased that the Admiral was watching and saw this abuse of a proud little winkle-brig.

A few days before Christmas I would be taken off to gather holly and ivy. The very best tree grew just below Lordy's Castle. Cheekily we would anchor just round the corner out of sight. Then my crew would creep silently ashore to return minutes later with sacks full of scarlet-berried holly. The gamekeepers patrolled the Estate day and night and this gave spice to the adventure. Charles and Janet did not forget to decorate me or the *Shamrock* each Christmas. A large bough of holly was always pulled to the top of our mastheads and we would pass Christmas Day quietly anchored side by side in that sheltered creek.

THE WORLD BEYOND

Down below the Bar the River Fal opens out into the Falmouth Roads. In fact it continues its course to the sea unseen in a deep channel in a large area of shallow water. This is where the oysters grow.

In summer it is a busy place. Fleets of dinghies race like gnats across the sheltered water. Yachts with their garish coloured sails are everywhere, but in the winter it is different. This is when the oyster boats go to work. With their patched and faded mainsails scandalised, and their tiny working jibs aback they drive sideways across the oyster beds. They are towing their heavy iron dredges and a trail of muddy water far astern shows where the dredge is hoeing over the sea bed. Aboard each boat a single oysterman bends over his tray 'culling out'. From the mass of dead shells he hunts the fat healthy oysters. Then when he has found them all he tips the tray and shoots the debris back over the side.

Now it is time to haul again, hand over hand, until the heavy iron dredge breaks the surface of the water. Then with a final heave it is emptied into the tray and the work continues all over again. When he has reached the end of the patch the oysterman hauls his dredges aboard. Up goes the peak of the mainsail and the foresail. The jib is let draw and the boat is sailed keenly back to begin towing once again.

This was the work which the *Shamrock* knew so well. She had earned her living like this for forty years.

Up a narrow little creek, past an old naval dockyard lay the boatyard. This was where the *Shamrock* and I were taken for repairs. It was run by a large and forceful shipwright. He had a single gold earring and was rather fierce. He reminded me of a pirate and I suspect he kept a parrot in his kitchen.

One spring they took the *Shamrock* down to the yard to have her engine removed. This was a large sullen piece of machinery which had started life aboard a cement mixer. It thumped and banged away emitting clouds of black smoke. Charles finally decided it must go the day he was towing me home from Falmouth. It was blowing hard from the east and the waves were curling up upon the rocks of Trefussis Point. I was made fast astern of the *Shamrock* and off we went. The engine spluttered and banged and just when the rocks were dead to leeward, a hundred yards off, she finally died. Desperately they scrambled sail upon the *Shamrock* and with yards to

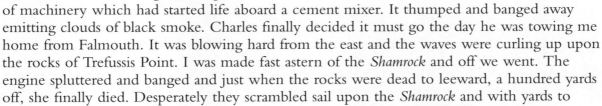

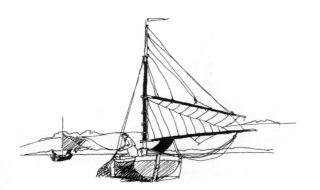

spare they clawed past the vicious rocks. Both the *Shamrock* and myself were in real danger that day – all because of a faulty engine.

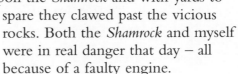

After that experience it was decided a sick engine was more of a liability than no engine at all. The *Shamrock* was sailed down to the boatyard and orders given to remove the engine. The Pirate set to with gusto and a large crowbar. The machinery was soon removed and the *Shamrock* became a true sailing boat once again.

It was a cold October day when Janet and Charles came to take the *Shamrock* home. The wind came hard up the narrow creek and the rain lashed the surface of the water. "I think we will give it a miss today," said Janet. "We'll see what it's like tomorrow." "Call yourself sailors?" roars the Pirate, "You're away today." With that he cast off the *Shamrock*'s warps and gave her a shove out into the tide. Somewhat chastened they turned the *Shamrock* down through the moorings and out into the Roads. The *Shamrock*, free of the drag of a propeller, felt young and sprightly, like a girl on her first date. She slipped through the water like a fish to join the other boats at the dredging.

At the north of the Roads stood the Black Rock and beyond this was the Bay. This was where we went after mackerel. Years ago this had been a large industry. Hundreds of brown-sailed luggers pursued the vast shoals that swam around the coasts of Cornwall, but now all that was finished. Modern factory fishing had seen to it that the mackerel had practically disappeared. Nonetheless, there were still enough for amateurs like me. In the autumn we would sail out into the Bay. Towing a spinner astern we would look for the signs. A flock of gulls perhaps, or better still a seal would show us where a shoal lay. As soon as the spinner took a fish the foresail would be pulled, Janet would run my peak off and I would lay (hopefully) drifting with the shoal. Then it was over the side with the 'feathers'.

This was a weighted line with four or five hooks baited with gaily-coloured rags. These were jogged up and down just clear of the bottom and if you were lucky the fish would strike, one to each hook. Then it was heave ho and up over my gunwale. With a deft flick the mackerel would be shaken off the hooks and lie flapping and gasping upon my floorboards.

One day we saw a ghost.

It was November, calm and misty. We were well amongst the mackerel and they were coming up thick and fast. Janet looked up from her work and saw another little boat, similarly fishing, driving down towards us. She was tarry black and old-fashioned looking. Her patched mizzen kept her head to wind. A single fisherman was busy jigging away at his lines. He was dressed in a yellow oilskin frock and wore a sou'wester. He had a large white beard and looked like one of those dour figures one sees in old photographs of nineteenth century fisher folk. Without a word or a wave he drove past and disappeared into the mist. The fishing number – FH 109 was quite plain upon the bows of the lugger. She was quite distinctive – and although we kept an eye out for her every time we sailed down to Falmouth and out into the Bay, we never saw her again.

THE FESTIVAL

One of the many pleasures of being a pretty little wooden boat are the friendly waves and salutes you receive wherever you go. Sail through a crowded mooring and someone always stops to watch you pass. They admire your lines, the set of your mainsail, or perhaps the neat and purposeful course you are sailing (yes, they are also there to watch when you get it wrong and make a mess of things!) Over the years, I, and my crew, have made many friends this way. Friends like these sharing beautiful places and enjoying the same experiences are the best sort of friends.

For some time now the interest in working boats, and in the culture of the sea, in the skills and endeavours it inspires, has been growing. Nowhere is the interest stronger than in Brittany upon the far western coast of France. That summer there was to be a great Festival of Traditional Boats at Douarnenez.

Janet and Charles decided that I should take part. I was hauled from the peace and tranquility of my mooring, loaded upon a trailer and hauled by road to Janet's home. Here I received the paint-up of a lifetime. My topsides were rubbed smooth and glossed until they sparkled in the sun. My mast and spars were varnished, coat after coat, until they shone like gold.

Janet sewed up a new flag for me. This was carefully copied from the Barge *Joy*'s bob. Instead of R for Rankin Janet sewed an H for Harker and mounted it upon the millers' old colours.

Finally when all was complete I was loaded once again upon that horrid trailer and rattled and bumped off to the Ferry Port. We arrived early in the morning and joined a queue of little boats all bound for the Festival. There was a gig from the Scillies with a muscular lady crew and a sixern all the way from Scotland. Her skipper was a Highlander with a kilt and hairy legs. We all piled aboard a large steamer and I spent the crossing quietly waiting in the cargo hold. Up in the saloon the Festival had made an early start. The gig ladies drank great foaming pints of lager and sang strange songs. The Scotsman played his bagpipes and everyone got very merry.

At last the steamer docked in France and I was dragged from the hold. Once again the torture on the trailer started and we ratted off overland in convoy with the other little boats.

In the evening we arrived in a busy town. The narrow streets were crowded and the houses were decorated with fishing nets. We wound our way down to the yacht harbour where I was to be unloaded. A cheery crew of Frenchmen lifted me from my trailer and swung me into the water. What a relief it was to be afloat again.

Janet and her crew stepped my mast and sorted out the tangle of my gear. Then we set sail and went off in search of the Festival. It was to be held in the Old Harbour around the

headland. It was dusk as I rounded the harbour wall and the sun was setting behind the old town. It was as if we had stepped back a hundred years into a world long gone. The harbour was jam-packed with every kind of traditional sailing boat. A great square rigger lorded it above all, her masts and yards rising high above the quay. There were smacks from my own coast, there were hookers from Ireland, tunneymen and sardiners from Northern France, galeases from Norway and trawlers from Germany. Pretty curvaceous botters from Holland lay alongside Bristol Channel pilot cutters. From the quayside came a cheery shout and there was Ben, the final member of my crew.

I sailed through this crowd, the very last boat it seemed to join the fleet, and found a berth alongside a little white lugger. We had arrived!

Next morning was grey and hard. A fresh breeze blew straight into the bay and rain squalls swept in from the west. No one was deterred and a mass of boats left the harbour all at once. They rowed, they sculled, they heaved and pulled. No one used an engine. Out in the bay a long swell rolled in from the Atlantic. I climbed slowly up the back of great waves and careered down the other side. All around me little boats were rising and falling on the heaving sea. One moment they would be perched upon the crest, the next moment only the tip of their mastheads were visible. A little varnished botter from Holland rode the seas like a clog, her young crew quite confident in their craft.

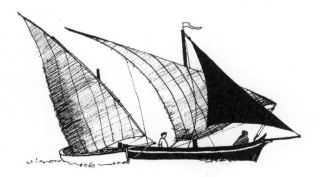

Janet flogged me out towards the open sea looking for the starting line of a race. Eventually she found an anchored yacht pitching and tossing. "Bonjour, bonjour," yelled a cheery Frenchman, "suivez les autres." He waved us on and we grimly followed three other little boats climbing up and down over the waves. It seemed a long way from the quiet creeks of my Cornish home. But soon I began to gain confidence and what is more we started to overhaul the other boats. We rounded the windward mark and bore away for the harbour. Neck and neck we raced with a little black crab boat from Caen. It did not matter that there were a dozen boats ahead of us. This was our own little race and each boat revelled in her ability in those long seas. Finally, we tore into the harbour and rounded up beneath the shelter of the breakwater. My crew was wet and cramped but exhilarated. They had sailed me through seas bigger than they had ever done before. They had baled constantly but I had shown them that I was capable and seaworthy. "Your builder would have been proud of you today," said Janet as she tied me up once again snug in a berth at the top of the harbour.

There were other sunny days when the wind blew gently off the land and the bay was calm and blue. Then all the great gathering of ships came out and sailed in a long procession round a circular course. The great bisquine *Cancalaise* raced neck and neck with the Brightlingsea smack *Sunbeam*. The Irish hooker *Morning Star* swept majestically by with a great white bow wave. The lateen-rigged oyster boats from Bordeaux skimmed across the

water like flying fish. And there was I, the *Joy*, a humble Mersea winklebrig playing my part too in this cavalcade of sail. In the centre of the bay was anchored a great Russian training ship, the *Sedov*. Suddenly, spontaneously, and with no apparent signal the fleet changed its course and steered down towards the *Sedov*. Leading this armada was the only Bermudan-rigged ship in the bay – the J class yacht *Velshida*. Her great triangular mainsail towered above the ships following her. It was like a swan leading her cygnets. I tucked myself in close upon the *Velshida*'s quarter and followed her course. We swept under the *Sedov*'s stern and gazed up at the towering spars of the square rigger. Overhead a helicopter clattered and roared whilst the world's press captured the moment.

The bay was filled that day by people and boats from all over Europe drawn together by a shared love of the sea. They admired each others' boats, studied the way they were handled, and marvelled at the variety of rigs. It did not seem possible that such differing combinations of sails and hull shapes could all produce, essentially, the same result. True, the purpose for which each ship had been built might be different. Some were built to tow trawls over the seabed, others to lie quietly to walls of drift nets. Some were built to carry cargoes to many different places. Some were built to carry pilots and tend upon the needs of other vessels. Some had been built merely to be towed and ferry passengers from one river bank to the other. But each one had been built to carry their crews safely and to deliver their cargoes wherever their Captains chose. The variety and ingenuity of their design was quite amazing.

RETIRED TO THE NORFOLK BROADS

The years slipped by pleasantly in my Cornish Creek. But then a change in my owners' fortunes ended all this. I left Cornwall and travelled east upon that hateful trailer. We passed to the north of London and for a moment I wondered, longingly, if we were going to return to my home in Essex. But this was not to be. Our destination was Norfolk and the Norfolk Broads.

Of course, I had heard of the Broads. In my barging days the coasting barges used to go away down to Yarmouth and up the River Yare to Norwich, although I never did. Miles of waterways and manmade lakes – the Broads provided a highway for the trading wherries and a playground for the summer yachtsmen.

It all sounded a little docile and somewhat of a comedown for a salty little winklebrig. Had I not ridden the Atlantic swell in the Bay of Douarnenez? I had cheated the sands of the Solway Firth and the fierce tides of the Thames Estuary. Was I now to be pensioned off and left to moulder in some reedy dyke?

These were the thoughts that passed through my mind as I travelled to my new home. I need not have worried. Although completely different from my Cornish Creek my Norfolk home had been chosen carefully. At the head of a long straight dyke was a small boatyard surrounded by pollarded willows. An old rowboat was sunken in the lawn by the office and planted full of flowers. Here they understood about elderly wooden boats and in fact in one corner of the yard a Norfolk wherry was being rebuilt plank by plank. When Charles asked for a mooring in this sheltered dyke the friendly proprietor asked what sort of boat it was. "I don't suppose it means much to you," he replied, "but the *Joy* is a Mersea winklebrig." "Ah but it does," said the proprietor. "You see my family started a boat building business in Mersea when I was a boy. I grew up at Mersea. We will have to find a space for a Mersea boat."

I was rolled down the slipway into the brown peaty waters of the dyke and made fast to the Staithe. The ducks were curious and came to look me over. I felt I was amongst friends.

That spring I set about discovering a new world. The River wound through broad open country. Black and white cattle grazed as far as the eye could see. Windmills dotted the landscape and the wide East Anglian skies have a special light all of their own. Along the river bank the rushes grew fresh and green. Hidden in their depths the coots and ducks had built their nests. If I sailed quietly down the edge my crew would suddenly come face to face with a fowl perched upon her nest. As the spring turned to summer proud ducks would lead their young across the water. Baby coots would squawk and plague their mothers for food. The grebes would carry their young upon their backs whilst the father was off diving for minnows. Down below in the murky depths patrolled the pike. Occasionally I would see a sullen swirl in the water. One day I watched a pair of coots followed by their young in line astern. Suddenly there was a splash and the hindmost babe just disappeared, dragged below by a prowling pike.

Janet bought me a new white topsail which caught the breeze above the reeds. I learned that you can sail close along the lee bank of a River, hugging close to the shore. The bow wave forms a cushion and seems to squeeze you up to windward. Late on a summer's evening we would sail with the last of the breeze up into my berth. As the moon rose and the wind finally died I would be made fast. There were other days in the winter when Charles pulled down the third reef in my mainsail and set the little jib. Then we would storm off down the dyke with our wash curling up the bank. There is rarely any sea to speak of in the river and so if carefully sailed I could stand a far harder blow than I could upon the saltwater. My old bones would creak and groan, rather like a wicker basket, as we flogged to windward. Sometimes when my skipper got too ambitious I would dip my lee rail. The water would flood aboard and he would let the mainsheet fly and so ease my course (if he had not we would both have ended upside down in the icy River). Then chastened, we would turn and run for home making the ducks squawk and swim in agitation all over the dyke. It was a happy retirement for an elderly brig. Each summer I would be swung out of the water by a crane and trundled into a long low boatshed. There I would receive a thorough paint-up and overhaul. The job was done quickly because if left in the summer sun my tired old planks would dry and split wide open. Each summer my name and the date was painted on the door of the shed. Joy '92; Joy '93; Joy '94.

Once upon a time there was a door such as this to the shed where I was built. As each barge left after being repaired her name was splashed upon that door. It became a roll call of familiar names – *Dawn, Ethel Maud, Nellie Parker. Hyacinth, Edme, Mirosa.* Alas, the shed was cleared in the name of progress and the door was burnt.

But in spite of this annual refit the years began to take their toll. Wood and particularly metal do not last together forever. One winter the dyke froze hard and I became trapped in the ice. All would have been well had I been left alone. There is no movement in the water at the head of a dyke and the ice would have done no damage on its own. But some vandals leapt aboard me and clambered across me to walk upon the ice. They stamped across my bilge and because the floorboards had been removed they drove holes in my old planks. When the thaw came I sank quietly and settled on the bottom. "I think she is trying to tell you something," said one of the shipwrights in the yard. Later I was hauled from the water and given an inspection.

The conclusion was sad. It was just no longer possible to carry out repairs to keep me sailing. It seemed I really was finished. And yet it was not quite so. After all, I still had my shape and my form. What difference is there in removing all my worn out planks and replacing them as opposed to capturing my shape and spirit and building afresh?

This is what Janet and Charles decided to do.

They returned to Maldon, where my story began so many years ago, and there just up river from that shed where I began my voyage they found David, a shipwright who had been bound apprentice to my builder. He came to Norfolk and carefully measured my form and captured my lines. Today, in another tarry shed, upon another bed of golden shavings, a new *Joy* is building.

55

GLOSSARY

Bilge	The bottom of a boat.
Centre-board	A plate hinged to drop vertically through the bottom of a boat to grip the water and stop her blowing sideways.
Cod End	The bag at the end of a trawl net where the fish are gathered.
Crab Fat	Navy slang for grey paint.
Crabbet	*(adjective)* Scottish word for bad tempered.
Davits	Curved arms mounted on the side of a ship up to which a Rowboat may be hauled.
Dolly	A heavy metal tool used to secure the head of a nail as a washer (or rove) is driven over the other end.
Dredge	Small net on an iron frame towed on the River's bottom to catch oysters.
Forestay	A wire rigged from the forward part of a ship's hull to support her mast.
Garboard Strake	The bottom plank nearest to the keel.
Gun whales	The timber around the top of an open boat.
Haaf net	A hand held net used to catch Salmon.
Hooker	An Irish Sailing Boat used for carrying cargoes between the Islands on the West Coast.
Iroko	An African hardwood.
Luff	*(noun)* The leading edge of a sail *(verb)* To steer a boat into the wind.

Oakum	Coarse fibre made from hemp used to fill the joints between ships planks also wadding in muzzle loading guns.
Painter	A length of rope attached to the bows of a Rowboat used to secure her.
Punt	In Cornwall an open rowing boat about 12ft long. In Essex a narrow flat bottom double ended boat used to pursue wildfowl.
Punt Gun	A large shot gun mounted upon a punt, often muzzle loaded.
Scandalise	Dropping the gaff to spill the wind from the sails.
Scull	*(verb)* To propel a boat with a single oar moved in a figure of eight fashion over her stern.
Setts	Square blocks of stone used to make roads.
Sheer	*(verb)* To move sideways across the tide.
Shram	Finely ground sea shells used in oyster cultivation or as chicken grit.
Shrouds	Rigging Wires from the sides of the boat to support the mast.
Skiff	Heavy built open boat about 20ft long used to ferry fish and oysters ashore.
Stern	The rear portion of a boat.
Stringer	A long length of wood running inside the length of an open boat upon which the thwarts sit.
Tholes	Short round lengths of wood placed vertically in a boat's rail to secure the oars whilst rowing.
Thwart	A seat going across a rowing boat.
Transom	A type of stern of a boat fastened square and vertical to the keel.
Windlass	A barrel placed horizontally across the bows of a ship used to wind up the anchor chain.

The builder of the *Joy*, Alf Last, working on a barge's boat in Cook's Shed, Maldon in the 1950s. The beautiful wine-glass transom is a signature feature.

Costings for a barge's boat in 1951 for Francis and Guilders. Note the wages – three shillings an hour is equal to fifteen pence per hour today.

Joy lying at Rankins Mill at Stambridge in 1950s.
Photograph by kind permission of Graham Brown of Coombe Creek, Cornwall. (The Admiral)

David Green sailing the *Joy* after major repairs and addition of a centreboard in 1966.

(Left) *Solvig*, a Swedish Galeas, 67 feet long bought out of trade from Fiskerbakshiel in 1966 and converted for charterwork by Peter Light.

(Above) Janet showing the ropes to Richard Harris and Jenny Agutter for the filming of 'The Snow Goose' by Paul Gallico in 1971.

(Left) *Iris* CK67 seen here in heavy weather well reefed down. A Colchester smack built in 1902 by Aldous of Brightlingsea. She was bought by Charles Harker in 1967.

(Above) Wreck of the *Iris* on Blackhall beach near Hartlepool in 1979.
Picture courtesy of Ian Dobson Photography, Seaham, Co. Durham

Saved from the quicksand athe the mouth of the river Pow, off the Solway Firth.

The rail of the *Joy* showing in the quicksand.

Joy after she emerged. Everything was well preserved, even Charle`s pipe which he left behind six years before.

Major repairs in the shed in Cornwall.
Charles fits a new apron.

Laying at her mooring in Coombe Creek off
the River Fal

Joy and *Shamrock* lying on the beach in Lamouth Creek.

(Left) *Shamrock* TO19, a Falmouth work boat built in Mevagissey in 1925.

(Below left) *Shamrock* and *Joy* about to pick up their moorings in Coombe Creek.

(Below) *Shamrock* and *Joy* sailing in company off Falmouth.

Tense faces of Janet, Charles and Ben sailing in the Bay of Douarnenez. This photo appeared on the front cover of Classic Boat Magazine, May 1989.
(By kind permission of Patrick Roach)

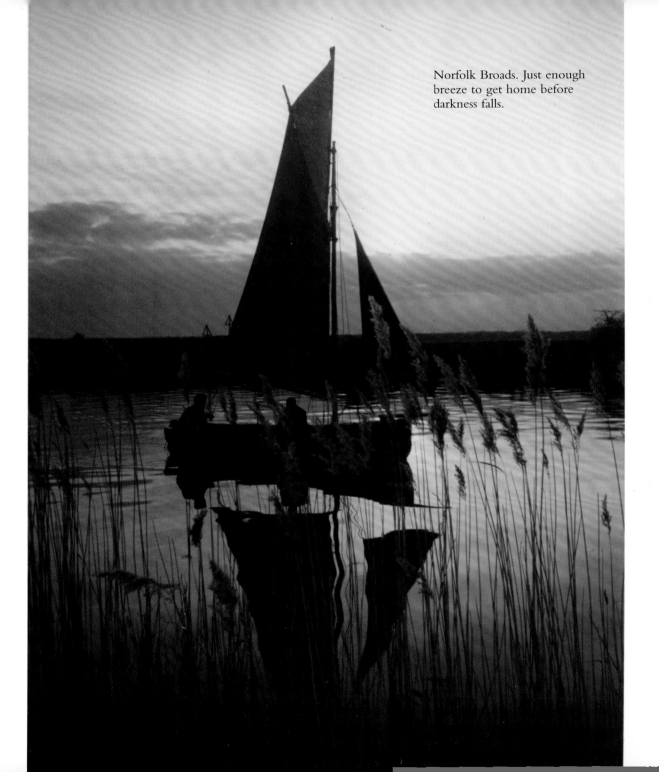

Norfolk Broads. Just enough breeze to get home before darkness falls.

Tied up
alongside
Thurne Mill.

New home at
Upton Dyke in
Norfolk. Jim
Lawrence, sailmaker
measures for new
sails in the ice.

The new *Joy* being built in David Patient's shed.